Contents

❖

Note to the Reader

❖

The Temple of My Familiar is a novel about the relationships of people to each other and to the world around them. It centers on the love stories of three couples, two of them young and one of them old. Throughout the novel, people tell stories about their own lives, their parents' lives and the lives of human beings from the beginning of time to the present day.

Every writer has a special voice. That is why we call our series *Writers' Voices*. We chose *The Temple of My Familiar* because Alice Walker's voice can be clearly heard as she tells the stories of living people and as she reaches back in history to times that can be remembered only in dreams.

In the part we have chosen, a young American black man named Suwelo listens to a tape recording made by an old woman named Miss Lissie. She tells two stories on the tape, both from a time beyond the beginning of written human history. In many cultures, stories about the beginning of the world are called myths.

Our book has several different chapters in addition to the selection itself. They provide background information that can help you in understanding the selection. You may choose to read some or all of these chapters before or after reading the selection.

Reading "About the Selection from *The Temple of My Familiar*" on page 10 will help you to begin thinking about what you will read in the selection. It will give you background about the characters and the setting of the story.

- If you would like more information about history and mythology and how they are related, look at the chapter called "About History and Myth" on page 55.

- Many readers enjoy finding out about the person who wrote the selection. Sometimes this information will give you more insight into the selection. You can find out more about Alice Walker in the chapter that begins on page 51.

If you are a new reader, you may want to have this book read aloud to you, perhaps more than once. Even if you are a more experienced reader, you may enjoy hearing it read aloud before reading it silently to yourself.

We encourage you to read *actively*. Here are some things you can do.

Before Reading

- Read the front and back covers of the book, and look at the cover illustration. Ask yourself what you expect the book to be about.

- Think about why you want to read this book. Perhaps you have heard of Alice Walker who wrote *The Color Purple* and who has won many prizes for her writing. Or you may be interested in reading a novel that looks at history and relationships among people from a black perspective.

- Look at the Contents page. See where you can find a map of the places where the selection takes place and other information. Decide what you want to read and in what order.

During Reading

- There may be words that are difficult to understand. Keep reading to see if the meaning becomes clear. If it doesn't, ask someone for the word or look up the word in a dictionary.

- Ask yourself questions as you read. For example, are Miss Lissie's stories similar to any others you may have heard? How are they similar? How are they different?

After Reading

- Think about what you have read. Did the selection change your thinking about earliest human times or about the way we treat animals?

- Talk with others about your thoughts.

- Try some of the questions and activities in "Questions for the Reader" on page 46. They are meant to help you discover more about what you have read.

The editors of *Writers' Voices* hope you will write to us. We want to know your thoughts about our books.

About the Selection from *The Temple of My Familiar*

❖

The word "familiar" comes from the word "family." When used to describe a person or an animal, "familiar" means "close friend" or "companion." In the selection, the familiars of the human characters are their animal companions.

In *The Temple of My Familiar*, a young black American man named Suwelo goes to Baltimore, Maryland, after his Uncle Rafe dies. Rafe has left his house and a small amount of money to Suwelo. While in Baltimore, Suwelo meets two of his uncle's best friends, Miss Lissie and Mr. Hal. These two elderly people have been close friends since childhood. They are married but are no longer lovers.

Miss Lissie and Mr. Hal become friendly

with Suwelo, and the three have many long, interesting conversations. Miss Lissie has a striking and strong personality. She is a born storyteller, and most of her stories concern lives she has lived before this one. Miss Lissie claims that her spirit has lived many, many lives since the beginning of time. In most of her lives she was a black woman, but in some she was a white man and even an animal.

The living of many lives is sometimes called reincarnation. Many religions, including the Hindu religion of India, believe in reincarnation.

As the selection begins, Miss Lissie has just died. Suwelo is listening to a tape recording of her voice. Miss Lissie tells Suwelo of her "dream memories" of the earliest human times. She explains how people and animals lived together as familiars in Africa. The place that she describes is like the Garden of Eden in some ways, but in other ways it is very different.

Perhaps the stories Miss Lissie tells will remind you of other stories, myths or fables you have heard or read. Perhaps they will make you think about the power of stories to make us see things in a new way.

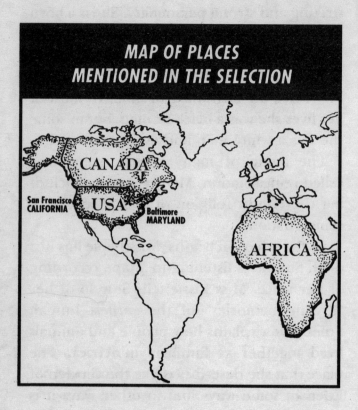

MAP OF PLACES MENTIONED IN THE SELECTION

CANADA

San Francisco
CALIFORNIA

USA

Baltimore
MARYLAND

AFRICA

Selected from

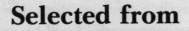

ALICE WALKER

"**H**ello, son."

It was Miss Lissie's voice, yet deeper, and weaker, *older*, than Suwelo remembered it. He adjusted the volume on the cassette player and sat down on the couch in front of it. On the left side of the sofa he'd set up his projector and filled it with the slides of Miss Lissie's work that Mr. Hal had sent him. After listening to her speak, he would have a look.

"By the time you get this," Miss Lissie's deep voice continued, "I will be somewhere and someone else. I have asked Hal to send it to you only upon my death, to which I almost look forward, knowing as I do that it is not the end, and being someone who enjoys hanging around, in spite of myselves. I regret leaving Hal, and am anxious as to our chances of coming together again; but that is all I do regret, and I have every faith we will meet again, and no doubt soon. For Hal and I have a lot more stuff to work out, and though we have been at it for so many years, and it's been hard labor, I can tell you, we've only just begun.

Miss Lissie cleared her throat.

"I am running on about this, Suwelo, because it is important, and true, but also because I am afraid to tell you how I know all this, to tell you my own news. Which is"— and here she took a long, slow breath—"that I lied when I told you I have always been a black woman, and that I can only remember as far back as a few thousand years.

"Of course I was from time to time a white woman, or as white as about half of them

are. I won't bore you with tales of the cen-
turies I spent sitting around wondering
which colored woman would do my floors.
Our menfolks were bringing them in all the
time. You'd go to sleep one night brotherless,
husbandless, fatherless, and in the morning
more than likely one of them would be back.
He'd be leading a string of some of the
wretchedest-looking creatures you ever saw.
Black, brown, red. Sometimes they looked
like Mongols or Chinese. You never knew
where in the world they came from. And he
wouldn't tell you. 'Got you some help,' was
the most he'd say, dropping his end of the
chain next to where he kept the dogs tied.

"He'd stick some savagely gorgeous trinket
on my neck or arm, surely made by witch-
craft, I'd think, but silver or, more likely,
gold, and start looking about for breakfast.

"I knew what a lady was supposed to do.
I clutched the front of my wrapper shut and
went to inspect the savages. I always turned
up my nose and made a pukey motion toward their filthy hair. They were so beaten
they could barely look at me.

"Over time, if *he* didn't pawn it, the thing

on my neck or arm would start talking to me. Especially whenever one of *them* looked at it. It took me years to understand that they knew that on my careless skinny, or fat, white arm I was wearing all the history, art, and culture of their own people that they and their children would ever see."

There was a pause. "Gold," said Miss Lissie thoughtfully, "the white man worships gold because it is the sun he has lost."

There was another pause, during which Suwelo leaned forward slightly and stared into the cassette spinning noiselessly round and round. In a moment, Miss Lissie drew in a labored breath and continued.

"Let me tell you a story," she said. "It is a dream memory, too, like the one I told you about my life with the cousins; but it is more tenuous even than that one, more faded. Weak. And that has been deliberate. I have repressed it for all I am worth. Regardless, it is still with me, because, like the other memories, it *is* me."

She paused, coughed, and said, "This was very long ago, indeed."

Suwelo leaned back against the cushions

of the couch, put his feet up on the coffee table in front of him, and placed his hands behind his head.

He thought he was ready.

"We lived at the edge of an immense woods," said Miss Lissie, "in the kind of houses, made of straw, that people built; insubstantial, really flimsy little things, somewhat fanciful, like an anthill or a spider's web, thrown up in a hour against the sun. My mother was queen of our group; a small group or tribe we were. Never more than a couple of hundred of us, sometimes fewer. But she was not 'queen' in the way people think of queens today. No, that way would have been incomprehensible to her, and horrid. I suppose she was what queens were originally, though: a wise woman, a healer, a woman of experience and vision, a woman superbly trained by her mother. A really good person, whose words were always heard by the clan.

"My mother kept me with her at all times, and she was always stroking me, rubbing into my skin various ointments she'd concocted from the flesh of berries and nuts that she found. As a small child I didn't notice any-thing wrong about spending so much time with my mother, nor was it ever unpleasant. Quite the contrary, in fact. Her familiar was an enormous and very much present lion; they went everywhere together. This lion also had a family of his own. There was a lot of visiting between us, and in the lion's little family of cubs I was always welcome.

"This perhaps sounds strange to you, Su-welo. About the lions, I mean. But it is true. This was long, long ago, before the animals had any reason to fear us and none whatever to try to eat us, which—the thought of eating us—I'm sure would have made them sick. The human body has been recognized as toxic, by the animals, for a very long time.

"In the Bible I know there's a line some-where about a time in the future when the earth will be at peace and the lion will lie down with the lamb. Well, that has already happened, and eventually it was to the det-riment of the lion.

"In these days of which I am speaking, people met other animals in much the same way people today meet each other. You were sharing the same neighborhood, after all. You used the same water, you ate the same foods, you sometimes found yourself peering out of the same cave waiting for a downpour to stop. I think my mother and her familiar had known each other since childhood; for that was the case with almost everyone. All the women, that is. For, strange to say, the women alone had familiars. In the men's group, or tribe, there was no such thing. Eventually, in imitation of the women and their familiars, companions, friends, or whatever you want to call them, the men learned to tame the barbarous forest dog and to get the occasional one of those to more or less settle down and stay by their side. I do not mean to suggest that the dogs were barbarous in the sense that we sometimes think of animals today as being 'red in tooth and claw.' No, they were barbarous because they simply lacked the sensibility of many of the other animals—of the lions, in particular; but also of the elephants and turtles, the vultures, the chimpanzees, the monkeys, orangutans, and giant apes. They were opportunistic little creatures, and basically lazy, sorely lacking in integrity and self-respect. Also, they lacked culture.

"It was an elegant sight, I can tell you, my mother and Husa walking along the river, or swimming in it. He was gigantic, and so beautiful. I am talking now about his spirit, his soul. It is a great tragedy today that no one knows anymore what a lion is. They think a lion is some curiosity in a zoo, or some wild thing that cares about tasting their foul flesh if they get out of the car in Africa.

"But this is all nonsense and grievous ignorance; as is most of what 'mankind' fancies it 'knows.' Just as my mother was queen because of her wisdom, experience, ability to soothe and to heal, because of her innate delicacy of thought and circumspection of action, and most of all because of her gentleness, so it was with Husa and his tribe. They were king of creation not because they were strong, but because they were strong and also gentle. Except to cull the sick or injured creatures from the earth, and to eat them, which was their role in creation, just as it is the role of the vulture to eat whatever has already died, they never used their awesome strength.

"We had fire by then. I say this because it was a recent invention; my mother's grandmother had not had it. Husa and his family would come of an evening to visit; they loved the fire; and there we'd all sprawl watching the changing embers and admiring the flames, well into the night, when we fell fast asleep. My mother and I slept close to Husa, and in the morning's chill his great heat warmed us.

"So I was not lonely, though at times I saw that other children regarded me strangely. But then, being children, they'd frequently play with me. I loved this. Our playing consisted very often of finding some new thing to eat. And we would roam for miles in search of whatever was easy to reach and ripe. It seemed to me there was everything anyone could imagine, and more than enough for twenty human and animal tribes such as ours. I wish the world today could see our world as it was then. It would see the whole tribe of creation climbing an enormous plum tree. The little brown and black people, for I had not yet seen myself as different; the monkeys, the birds, and the things that today have vanished but which were bright green and sort of a cross between a skunk and a squirrel. There we'd be, stuffing ourselves on plums—little and sweet and bright yellow. Husa would let us stand on his back to reach the high inner branches. If we were eating for a long time, Husa would lie on the ground yawning, and when we were full, the monkeys, especially, would begin a game, which was to throw plums into Husa's yawning mouth. It was curious to see that no matter how rapidly we threw the plums into his mouth, Husa never swallowed one and never choked. He could raise the back of his tongue, you see, like a kind of trapdoor, and the plums all bounced off it.

"What does not end, Suwelo? Only life itself, in my experience. Good times, specific to a time and place, always end. And so it was with me. The time arrived when I was expected to mate. In our group this was the initiation not only into adulthood, but into separation from the women's tribe—at least from the day-to-day life of it that was all one had ever known. After mating and helping his mate to conceive, a man went to live with men. But this was not a hardship, since the men's encampment was never more than half a day's journey from our own, and there was always, between the two tribes, the most incessant visiting. Why didn't they, men and women, merge? It simply wasn't thought of. People would have laughed at the person who suggested it. There was no reason why they should merge, since each tribe liked the arrangement they had. Besides, everyone— people and other animals—liked very much to visit. To be honest, we loved it. That was our TV. And so it was well to have other people and other animals *to* visit.

"Though I hated the thought of leaving my mother, I knew I could still see her whenever I wanted to, and I also knew that the men in the men's tribe were ready to be my father. For no one had a particular father. That was impossible, given the way the women chose their lovers, freely and variously. The men found nothing strange in this, any more than the women did. Why should they? Lovemaking was considered one of the very best things in life, by women and men; of course it would have to be free. See what I mean about songs?" Miss Lissie chuckled. "Besides, when a young man arrived in the tribe of the men, they were at long last given an opportunity—late, it's true—to mother. Fathering *is* mothering, you know.

"There was a girl I liked, who liked me back. This was a miracle. And at the proper time, the day before the coming up of the full moon, she and I were sent to pick plums together. I remember everything about that day: the warmth of the sun on our naked bodies, the fine dust that covered our feet. . . . Her own little familiar, a serpent, slid alongside us. Serpents then were different than they are now, Suwelo. Of course almost everything that was once free is different today. Her familiar, whom my friend called Ba, was about the thickness of a slender person's arm and had small wheel-like extendable feet, on which it could raise itself and whir about, like some of those creatures you see in cartoons; or, retracting these, it could move like snakes move today. It could also extend and retract wings, for all serpents that we knew of at that time could fly. It was a lovely companion for her, and she loved it dearly and was always in conversation with it. I remember the especially convoluted and wiggly trail Ba left behind in the dust, in its happy anticipation of eating fresh plums. . . . Later that day there was the delicious taste of sun-warmed plums in our mouths. We were, all three of us, chattering right along, and eating, and feeling very happy.

"I was not to be happy long; none of us was. Eventually I had my friend in my arms, and one of her small black nipples, as sweet as any plum and so like my mother's, was in my mouth, and I was inside her. It was everything I'd ever dreamed, and much more than I'd hoped. But it was not, I think, the same for her. When I woke up, she was wide awake, simply sitting there quietly, stroking Ba, who was lazily twisting his full self around and around her beautiful knees. The sun was still above the treetops, for I remember that the light was golden, splendidly perfect, but even as I watched, it began rapidly going down.

"And then, when I looked down at myself,

I saw that while I was sleeping she had rubbed me all over with the mixture of dark berries and nut fat my mother always used, which I realized had been hidden beneath the plum tree. And for the first time I could ask someone other than my mother what it was for. My mother had said it was to make my skin strong and protect it from the sun. And so, I asked my friend. And *she* said it was to make me look more like everyone else.

" 'You look like you don't have a skin, you know,' she said. 'But you do have one.'

"I was thrown completely by this, coming as it did after our first lovemaking. It seemed to indicate a hideous personal deficiency that I didn't need to hear about just then, on the eve of becoming a man in the tribe of men. Right away I thought: Is this how they'll see me as well?

"She took me gently by the hand and we walked to a clear reflecting pool not far away. We'd often bathed there. And she scooped up a handful of water and vigorously scrubbed my face; then we bent down over the water, and there my friend was, looking very much like my mother and her mother and the sisters and brothers and aunts of the village—all browns and blacks, with big dark eyes. And there was I—a ghost. Only, we knew nothing of ghosts, so I could not even make that comparison. I did look as though I had no skin.

"It was the first time I'd truly seen myself as different. I cried out in fear at myself. Weeping, I turned and ran. My friend came running after me. For it had not been her intention to hurt. She was taking over my mother's duty in applying the ointment, and was only trying to be truthful and help me begin to face reality.

"All I could think of was hiding myself— my kinky but pale yellow hair, the color of straw in late summer, my pebble-colored eyes, and my skin that had no color at all. I ran to a cave I knew about not far from the plum tree. And I threw myself on the floor, crying and crying.

"She came in behind me, the mess of berries and nut fat in a bamboo-joint container in her hand. She tried to talk to me, to soothe me, to spread the stuff over me. I knocked it away from me; it rolled over the earthen floor. During this movement, I suddenly caught sight of my member and saw that the color that had been there before we made love had been rubbed off during our contact. The sight shamed me. I ran outside the cave and grabbed the first tree leaves I saw and slapped them over myself.

"But then I realized it was my whole body that needed covering, not just my penis. My friend was still running around behind me, trying to comfort me. She was crying as much as I was, and beating her breasts. For we learned mourning from the giant apes, who taught us to feel grief anywhere around us, and to reflect it back to the sufferer, and to act it out. But now this behavior made me sick. I picked up a stick and chased her away. She was so shocked to see me use a stick in this way that she seemed quite happy to drop her sympathies for me and run. But as she turned to run, her familiar, seeing her fright and its cause, extended both its clawed feet and its wings and flew up at me. In my rage I struck it, a brutal blow, with my club, so hard a blow that I broke its neck, and it fell without a sound to the ground. I couldn't believe I had done this. Neither could my friend. She ran back, though she was so afraid, and scooped Ba's broken body up in her arms. The last I saw of her was her small, naked, dark brown back, with Ba's limply curling tail, which was beginning to change colors, dangling down her side.

"I never made it into the men's tribe. I never went back to my mother. The only one from my childhood I ever saw again was Husa. Perhaps he came to look for me as a courtesy to my mother. He found me holed up in a cave far, far from our encampment, my hair in kinky yellow locks, which resembled his, actually; my stone gray eyes wild with pain. He came up to me and rested a warm paw on my shoulder and breathed gently into my face. The smell made me almost faint from love and homesickness. Then he proceeded to lick me all over, thoroughly, as he would wash one of his cubs, with his warm pink tongue. I realized that night, sleeping next to Husa, that he was the only father I had ever known or was ever likely to know. And so, I felt, I had left my mother to join the men after all.

"Of course Husa could not stay forever. But he stayed long enough. Long enough to go on long walks with me, just as he did with my mother. Long enough to share fires— which I knew he loved, and so forced myself to make. Long enough to share sunrises and sunsets and to admire giant trees and sweet-smelling shrubs. For Husa greatly appreciated the tiniest particle of the kingdom in which he found himself. He taught me that there was another way of being in the world, away from one's own kind. Indeed, he reconciled me to the possibility that I had no 'own kind.' And though I missed my mother terribly, I knew I would never go back. It hurt me too much to know that everyone in our group had always noticed, since the day I was born, that I was different from anyone who had ever lived.

"One day, after a kill, Husa brought the remains, a draggle of skin, home to me. With a stone I battered it into a shape that I could drape around myself. I found a staff to support me in my walks and to represent 'my people.'

"Husa left.

"And now I gradually made a discouraging discovery. The skin that Husa gave me, which covered me so much more effectively than bark or leaves, and which I could tie on in a manner that would stay, frightened all the animals with whom I came in contact. In vain did I try to explain how I came by it, how much I needed it. That it was a gift, a leftover, from Husa the lion, who harmed no creature, ever, but was only the angel of mercy to those things in need of death. But what animal could comprehend this new thing that I was? That I, a creature with a skin of its own—for though I looked skinned, they could smell I was not—was nonetheless walking about in one of theirs? They ran from me as if from plague. And I was totally alone for many years, until, in desperation, I raided the litter of a barbarous dog, and got myself companionship in that way."

❖

The tape ran on and on, without Miss Lissie's voice. Suwelo rose from the couch and

peered at the spinning cassette. He was about
to stop it, and see if it should be turned over,
when Miss Lissie's voice continued. She
sounded somewhat rested, as if she'd taken
a long break.

"You may wonder," she said, "why I repressed this memory. And, by the way, I
don't know what else became of me, or of
my dog. It is hard to believe my mother never
searched for me, never found me. That I
lived the rest of my days in that place without
a mate. Perhaps my mate did come to me,
and perhaps she brought our child, which
must have been odd-looking; for she loved
me, of that I had no doubt, and perhaps we
began a new tribe of our own. That, anyway,
is *my* fantasy." She laughed. "It is also the
fantasy upon which the Old Testament
rests," she said, "but without any mention of
our intimacy with the other animals or of the
brown and black colors of the rest of my
folks.

"I will tell you why I repressed this memory. I repressed it because of Hal. But, Suwelo, there is more; for that is not the only
lifetime I have given up, or, I should say,

that I have deliberately taken away from myself. In each lifetime I have felt forced to shed knowledge of other existences, other lives. The times of today are nothing, nothing, like the times of old. The time of writing is so different from the so much longer time of no writing. People's very eyes are no longer the same. The time of living separate from the earth is so much different from the much longer time of living with it, as if being on your mother's breast. Can you imagine a time when there was no such thing as dirt? It is hard for people to comprehend the things that I remember. Even Hal, the most empathetic of fellow travelers, up to a point, could not follow some of the ancient and pre-ancient paths I knew. I swallowed past experiences all my life, as I divulged those that I thought had a chance, not of being believed—for no one has truly, truly believed me; at least that is my feeling, a bitter one, most of the time—but of simply being imagined, fantasied.

"Suwelo, in addition to being a man, and white, which I was many times after the time of which I just told you, I was also, at least once, myself a lion. This is one of those dream memories so frayed around the edges that it is like an old, motheaten shawl. But I can still sometimes feel the sun on my fur, the ticks in my mane, the warm swollen fullness of my tongue. I can smell the injured and dying kin who are in need of me to bring them death. I can feel the leap in my legs, the stretch in my belly, as I bound toward them and stun them, in great mercy, with a blow. I can taste the sweet blood as my teeth puncture their quivering necks, breaking them instantly, and without pain. All of this knowledge, all of this remembrance, is just back of my brain.

"But the experiences I best remember were sometime after the life in which I knew Husa. It was, in fact, a terrible, chaotic time, though it had started out, like the eternity everyone knew, peacefully enough. Like Husa I was friends with a young woman and her children. We grew up together and frequently shared our favorite spots in the forest, or stared by night into the same fire. But this way of life was rapidly ending, for somehow or other by the time I was fully grown, and big, as lions tend to be, the men's camp and the women's had merged. And they had both lost their freedom to each other. The men now took it on themselves to say what should and should not be done by all, which meant they lost the freedom of their long, undisturbed, contemplative days in the men's camp; and the women, in compliance with the men's bossiness, but more because they now became emotionally dependent on the individual man by whom man's law now decreed they must have all their children, lost their wildness, that quality of homey ease on the earth that they shared with the rest of the animals.

"In the merger, the men asserted themselves, alone, as the familiars of women. They moved in with their dogs, whom they ordered to chase us. This was a time of trauma for women and other animals alike. Who could understand this need of men to force us away from woman's fire? And yet, this is what they did. I remember the man and the dog who chased me away; he had a large club in one hand, and in the other, a long, sharply pointed stick. And how sad I was to leave my friend and her children, who were crying bitterly. I think I knew we were experiencing one of the great changes in the structure of earth's life, and it made me very sorrowful, but also very thoughtful. I did not know at the time that man would begin, in his rage and jealousy of us, to hunt us down, to kill and eat us, to wear our hides, our teeth, and our bones. No, not even the most cynical animal would have dreamed of that. Soon we would forget the welcome of woman's fire. Forget her language. Forget her feisty friendliness. Forget the yeasty smell of her and the warm grubbiness of her children. All of this friendship would be lost, and she, poor thing, would be left with just man, screaming for his dinner and forever murdering her friends, and with man's 'best friend,' the 'pet' familiar, the fake familiar, his dog.

"Poor woman!

"But to tell you the truth, Suwelo, I was not sorry to go. For I was a lion. To whom harmony, above everything, is sacred. I could see that, merged, man and woman were in for an eternity of strife, and I wanted no part of it. I knew that, even if man had let us remain beside woman's fire he would be throwing his weight around constantly, and woman being woman, every so often would send pots and pans flying over our heads; this would go on forever. An unbearable thought; as a lion, I could not bear loud noises, abrupt changes in behavior, voices raised in anger. *Evilness.* No lion could tolerate such things. It is our nature to be nonviolent, to be peaceful, to be calm. And ever to be fair in our dealings; and I knew this would be impossible in the present case, since the animals, except for the barbarous dogs, clearly preferred woman, and would always have been attempting to defend her. Lions felt that, no matter the circumstance, one must be dignified. In consorting with man, as he had become, woman was bound to lose her dignity, her integrity. It was a tragedy. But it was a fate lions were not prepared to share.

"In subsequent periods lions moved farther and farther away from humans, in search of peace. There were tribes with whom we kept connections, in that we taught, and they learned from us. What did they learn? They learned that rather than go to war with one's own kind it was better to pack up and remove oneself from the site of contention. That as long as there is space in which to move there is a possibility of having uncontested peace. There are tribes living today in South Africa who have never come to blows with each other for a thousand years. It is because of what they learned from the lions.

"For thousands of years our personalities were known by all and appreciated. In a way, we were the beloved 'uncles' and 'aunts'—interesting visitors, indulgent playmates, superb listeners, and thoughtful teachers—of the human tribe, which, fortunately, could never figure out, not for a long, long time, anyhow, any reason why we should be viewed as completely different from them and separate from them. Only gradually did we fade into myth—all that was known of us previously, that is.

"Now," said Miss Lissie, whose voice was again becoming tired, "there were but two things on earth Hal truly feared. He feared white people, especially white men, and he feared cats. The fear of the white man was less irrational than the fear of cats, but they were both very real fears to Hal. You could make him back up twenty miles simply by asking him to hold a cat. And he arranged his life so that if he ever saw a white man, it was by accident, and also very separate from his personal life, an unheralded and unwelcome event. So how could I tell him all of who I was? By now Hal is like my son to me, and I couldn't bear it if he hated me. For such fear as Hal's *is* hatred.

"And so, I never told him. How could I say it? *Yo*, Hal, I was a white man; more than once; they're probably still in there somewhere. *Yo*, Hal, I was also, once upon a time, a very large cat."

Miss Lissie chuckled. Then laughed and laughed. Suwelo did too. Her laughter was the last sound on that side of the tape.

"But if you love someone, you want to share yourself, or, in my case," said Miss Lissie—and Suwelo imagined her wiping her eyes, still smiling—"you want to share your-

selves. But I was afraid. Maybe there's always a part of the self that we hide, deny, deliberately destroy.

"But oh, how we love the person who affirms even that hateful part of us. And it was for affirming these split-off parts of my memory that I loved your uncle Rafe. Rafe, unlike Hal, was afraid of no one. He thought white people the most pathetic people who ever lived. Ruling over other people, he said, automatically cuts you off from life. And to try to rule over colored people, who, anybody could see, were life itself! He was more puzzled than annoyed when otherwise intelligent-looking and -acting white people called him 'boy' or 'nigger.' He was always hoping for a little better from them than he ever got. But that was because he could easily see some of himself in them, though, when looking back at him, white people apparently saw . . . But he often wondered just *what* it was that they saw. What they let themselves see. Were they blind to his very *being*, as he himself was blind to the being of a fly? To him, their constant imperative to 'civilize' us was in fact a need to blind and deaden us to their own extent.

"I told Rafe everything; and he took me north, to Canada, in the summers, to be around white people; and he took me to more zoos than I have the heart to mention. This was part and parcel of his making love to me, you see, taking me to those places of which I was, myself, most afraid. You cannot imagine the feeling I had the first time I sat down to dinner in a restaurant that was filled with white people, white people who only stared at us and whispered among themselves, but did not, as they would have done in the South, rush to throw us out of the building, or perhaps beat us up or even lynch us.

"I remember that Rafe ordered meat. Some kind of duck, I think. And when it came, he saw the look on my face. I could never eat meat among white people; of that I was sure; my stomach heaved at the thought of it. Rafe and I ate mashed potatoes and salad, and he said to me, in that deep, caressing, *sweet* Negro voice of his: 'Well, Lissie, have a *good* look.'

"And I could see how they'd closed themselves off, these descendants, there at the 'top of the heap,' and how isolated they were.

They were completely without wildness, and they had forgotten how to laugh. They had also forgotten, I was to discover on our many trips, how to dance and sing. They haunted black people's dance halls and churches, trying to 'pick up' what they'd closed off in themselves. It was pitiful.

"In a way, I preferred the zoos. Though I hated them with all my heart, naturally. But at the zoo, at least there were no illusions about who was free and who was not. The lions were always in cages too small for them. And it had never occurred to anyone that, cut off from life year upon year, as they were, with nothing whatever to do, the least that could be done was to build them a fire. It was heartbreaking—to watch them pace, to smell the sour staleness of their coats and of their cells, to hear the hysteria in their roar, to watch them devour a perfectly healthy animal that had been raised for 'meat' and killed on an assembly line by machine. It was horrible. It was a fate the most imaginative and cynical preancient lion could not have imagined. And now, as a presence in the modern world, I am thankful for this.

"The most abominable thing to see was their faces. Slack, dull, unintelligent, *unthoughtful*. Stupefied from boredom, gross from the degradation of dependency. To every zoo—colored could go even to the one in Baltimore, after a long struggle; but only on maid's day off, Thursday—I carried a large mirror. Anyone else would have thought this strange, but not Rafe. He helped me carry it and hold it up outside the cages. A restless lion would amble up to the bars and have a look at himself. This was usually the first and only look at himself he'd ever had. I held my breath.

"Would there be a flicker of recognition? Even of interest? Did the lion inside the body of the lion see itself? Though I myself had the body of a woman, I could still see my lion inside. Would they see that? Would they see the old nobility, the old impatience with inferiors? The old grace?

"One or two of them saw something. But it only made them sad. They slunk back to a corner of their cages and put their heads down between their paws. Of course I wanted to leap through the bars to comfort them. I wanted to destroy the bars.

"Rafe carried me back home, a pitiful wreck, after these excursions, and put me to bed. He and Hal and Lulu [our daughter] would come in to kiss me good night; and when Rafe was turning to go, I would grasp his hand—such a good, steady, clean brown hand it was. He would sit down on the bed without a word and take off his shoes.

"Your uncle Rafe was an incomparable lover, Suwelo. And I have missed him so much, I have sometimes longed to meet up with him again, which I know is not likely; there is little need for him to come back. He loved the total me. None of my selves was hidden from him, and he feared none of them. Sometimes, when I would get 'on my high horse,' as he called it, when I was ordering everybody around and complaining that nobody knew anything or could do anything right but me, he'd grin and say, 'You sure are showing your white tonight!' And I'd feel how ridiculous I was being, and laugh.

"Or, sometimes at a party, I'd realize the other people were a bunch of lowlifes, and

I'd leave. Just stroll out the door. Rafe would come after me and look at me prowling along the sidewalk aching for distance, and peace, and calm; disgust at the party's members still on my face, and he'd say, 'Baby, the lion in winter's got nothing on you!'

"And of course he knew and appreciated all the other selves, and could call them by name, too.

"So, loving Rafe and being loved by Rafe was the experience of many a lifetime. And very different from being loved by Hal, even when our passion for each other was at its height, Hal loved me like a sister/mystic/warrior/woman/mother. Which was nice. But that was only part of who I was. Rafe, on the other hand, knowing me to contain everybody and everything, loved me wholeheartedly, as a goddess. Which I was."

Questions for the Reader

❖

Thinking About the Story

1. What did you think about the selection from *The Temple of My Familiar*? What did you like or not like?

2. Did the events or people in the selection become important or special to you? Write about or discuss this.

3. What do you think were the most important things Alice Walker wanted to say in the selection?

4. Were any parts of the selection difficult to understand? If so, you may want to read or listen to them again. Discuss with your learning partners possible reasons why they were difficult.

Thinking About the Writing

1. How did Alice Walker help you see, hear and feel what happened in the selection? Find the words, phrases or sentences that did this best.

2. Writers think carefully about their stories' characters and events. In writing this selection, what do you think Alice Walker felt was most important? Find the parts of the story that support your opinion.

3. Which character in the selection was most interesting to you? How did Alice Walker help you learn about this person? Find the places in the selection where you learned the most about this person.

4. In the selection, Alice Walker uses monologue, where one person talks the whole time. Did Miss Lissie's monologue help the story seem true? How?

5. In the stories she tells about her past lives, Miss Lissie has been a black woman, a white man, a white woman and even a lion. Think about why Alice Walker has

Miss Lissie tell stories from different points of view. Think about what each story means to you. Go back to the story and find the parts that created meaning most vividly for you.

Activities

1. Were there any words that were difficult for you in the selection from *The Temple of My Familiar*? Go back and try to figure out their meanings. Discuss what you think each word means, and why you made that guess. Discuss with your teacher or another student how you are going to remember each word. Some ways to remember words are to put them on file cards, or write them in your journal or create a personal dictionary. Be sure to use the words in your writing in a way that will help you to remember their meanings.

2. How did you help yourself understand the selection? Did you ask yourself ques-

tions? What were they? Discuss these questions with other people who have read the same selection, or write about them in your journal.

3. Talking with other people about what you have read can increase your understanding of it. Discussion can help you organize your thoughts, get new ideas and rethink your original ideas. Discuss your thoughts about the selection with someone else who has read it. Find out if your opinions are the same or different. See if your thoughts change as a result of this discussion.

4. After you finish reading or listening, you might want to write down your thoughts about the book. You could write a book review, or a letter to a friend who might be interested in *The Temple of My Familiar*. You could write your reflections on the book in your journal, or you could write about topics the book has brought up that you want to explore further.

5. Did reading the selection give you any ideas for your own writing? You might want to write about:

- Your dreams, which are your own private myths. After you have a dream, write it down. Then choose one or two things from the dream and discuss what they mean to you.

- How you feel about animals or your friendship with one particular animal.

- A myth you have read or heard. You might want to write about what you think the myth means, or you might want to retell it in a way you think is better.

6. If you could talk to Alice Walker, what questions would you ask about her writing? You might want to write the questions in your journal.

About
ALICE WALKER

❖

Alice Walker was born on February 9, 1944, in Eatonton, Georgia. She was the youngest of the eight children of Minnie and Willie Lee Walker. The family were sharecroppers, and every family member picked cotton. Her father made about $300 a year, and her mother earned 75 cents a day as a maid.

Although neither of her parents went past the fifth grade, Alice Walker was sent to school at an early age and became an avid learner. In an interview in *Essence* magazine, she said, "I used to think I had just been dropped into my family, and I didn't know by whom or what. I think I started writing just to keep from being so lonely, from being so much the outsider."

When Alice was eight years old, one of her brothers shot her in the right eye with a BB gun. She lost the sight in that eye, which developed scar tissue. She was self-conscious about her eye and was shy and retiring. She began writing poems around this time. When she was fourteen, the scar tissue was removed and she became, as she once said, "a changed person."

Graduating at the top of her high school class in 1961, Alice Walker received a scholarship to Spelman College in Atlanta, Georgia. Two years later, with another scholarship, she went to Sarah Lawrence College in Bronxville, New York.

After college, from the late 1960s to the middle 1970s, Walker taught at colleges in Mississippi. She also worked for voter registration and in the Head Start program. In 1967 she married Melvyn Leventhal, a white civil rights lawyer. Her daughter, Rebecca, was born in 1969.

Walker has written four novels, two collections of short stories, five volumes of poetry and two collections of essays (see "Alice Walker's Other Books" on page 60). Her central theme is the black woman's struggle for spiritual wholeness and for sexual, political and racial equality. Yet Walker's message of hope and the possibility of change speaks to people of both sexes and all races.

Walker's books also reflect her concern with other issues, such as animal rights, the antinuclear movement and the environment.

The Color Purple is Alice Walker's most famous book. It is the story of Celie, a black woman who writes letters to God about her life. The book has been translated into 22 languages, and more than 4 million copies are in print around the world. Published in 1982, *The Color Purple* was made into a movie directed by Steven Spielberg three years later. The book and the movie have been the subject of controversy. Some people feel that the story wrongly paints a negative image of black men.

Walker won several literary awards for *The Color Purple*, including the Pulitzer Prize. She was the first black woman novelist to win the Pulitzer Prize for fiction.

In the mid-1970s, Walker lived in Brooklyn, New York. After her divorce in 1977, she moved to San Francisco, California, where she lives today. Her companion is

Robert Allen, a black writer, editor and activist.

Alice Walker spent eight years writing *The Temple of My Familiar*, which was published in 1989.

About
History and Myth

❖

Every culture has its myths:

- The ancient Egyptians had the goddess Isis and her husband-brother, Osiris, who represented the creative forces of nature.

- The Greeks had Zeus, the king of the gods; Aphrodite, the goddess of love; Ares, the god of war; and many others.

- The major figure in African Zulu and Xhosa mythology is Unkulunkulu, which means "The Very Old," the first man or ancestor of the human race.

- Ancient Native American mythic figures include the Master of Animals and the Corn Mother.

- Japanese myths center around the *kami*, or gods.

According to Joseph Campbell, one of the foremost experts on the subject, "Myths are clues to the spiritual potentialities of the human life." Campbell also said, "Myths and dreams come from the same place." He said that a dream is a private myth and that a myth is a society's dream.

Myths are usually not based solely on fact but arise in large part from the human imagination. Yet people often believe them as though they are true facts. Myths are like history in that they attempt to explain the world and the past from a particular culture's point of view.

History can also be seen as a kind of mythology because it can be seen from one point of view or another. Historians often view the world from their own personal vantage points. Even though most people think that what they read in a history book is the only truth, there can be many versions of one event.

In American schools today, there is a movement toward rewriting history textbooks. Until recently, American history focused on the white European males who settled in North America and who dominate the political life of the United States today. Those who want to rewrite the books want to include the contributions of all the people who make up American society: blacks, Spanish-speaking people, Native Americans, Asians and women of all races.

In many cases, the rewriting will result in telling the same story but in a very different way. For example, a Native American's account of the settling of the United States would be very different from that of a white European man.

In a 1989 interview in *The Progressive* magazine, Alice Walker said, "It's amazing to me that the white male establishment...really seems to believe that because they buy the myth...that the only thing worth knowing is what they produced—it's amazing to me that they think we should think it. We don't.... Whatever their world view is, it is certainly not shared by me."

Just as history can be rewritten—for a change in emphasis or to focus on a different point of view—so myths can be changed or reinvented, which is what Alice Walker does in *The Temple of My Familiar*. She makes up stories to present her ideas of how society evolved and why relationships between people are the way they are.

In the selection from *The Temple of My Familiar*, the story of the young boy who discovers he has white skin is a myth that Walker has created. In that story, the black people are the dominant society, and the sad white boy feels himself to be an outcast because of the color of his skin.

The story describes something that might have happened thousands of years ago. In telling it, Walker casts a new light on the origins of relations between the races. This is a mythological explanation written by a black person.

She does the same thing in having Miss Lissie tell the story of her life as a lion. In imagining the story from the lion's point of view, Walker makes the reader see things in a new way.

In an interview in *Essence* magazine, Alice Walker said about *The Temple of My Familiar*, "If the tribal peoples of the earth wrote novels, this is what one would look like. It affirms the validity, the force and the health of the oral tradition. *Our* tradition. For the first time in our history, Black people are losing their own stories, because we watch too much television. We are losing the stories that kept us healthy.

"The so-called Uncle Remus tales and the Brer Rabbit tales are all moral ones. They kept us aware of who we are, who the opposition is and how to keep going. One way of getting back to that tradition is for the older people to speak and for the younger people to listen. And there should be real truth in this exchange."

Alice Walker's
Other Books

❖

Novels

The Third Life of Grange Copeland (*1970*). The effects of poverty and racism on three generations of a black sharecropping family.

Meridian (*1976*). A young woman named Meridian is caught in the conflict between traditional black values and the ideas of the black power movement.

The Color Purple (*1982*). The story of Celie, a black woman who writes letters to God about the brutality of her life. Although victimized and abused, Celie survives as a stronger person with the help of the positive relationships in her life.

Short Stories

In Love and Trouble: Stories of Black Women (*1973*). Stories about the effects of the sexism and racism against which black women must struggle.

You Can't Keep a Good Woman Down: Stories (*1981*). Stories about abortion, pornography and rape in which Walker says that relationships are both personal and political.

Poetry

Once: Poems (*1968*). Written while Walker was in college, these poems are about a trip she made to Africa, the civil rights movement, love and suicide.

Revolutionary Petunias and Other Poems (*1973*). Poems on love, individualism and revolution that reflect Walker's years of work as a civil rights activist and teacher.

Good Night, Willie Lee, I'll See You in the Morning: Poems (*1979*). Poetry about family and friendship, and the changing of love relationships between women and men.

Horses Make a Landscape Look More Beautiful: Poems (*1986*). Poems about current social issues.

Her Blue Body Everything We Know: Earthling Poems 1965–1990 Complete (*1991*). A collection of Walker's poems from 1965 to 1990.

Essays

In Search of Our Mothers' Gardens: Womanist Prose (*1983*). In this collection, Walker introduces the word "womanist" as a more dignified alternative to the phrase "black feminist." Some of the essays concern Walker's own life story.

Living by the Word: Selected Writings 1973–1987 (*1988*). Among other topics, these essays are about black women's sexuality and animal liberation, two important ideas in *The Temple of My Familiar*.

Three series of good books for all readers:

Writers' Voices—A multicultural, whole-language series of books offering selections from some of America's finest writers, along with background information, maps, glossaries, questions and activities and many more supplementary materials for readers. Our list of authors includes: Amy Tan • Alex Haley • Alice Walker • Rudolfo Anaya • Louise Erdrich • Oscar Hijuelos • Maxine Hong Kingston • Gloria Naylor • Anne Tyler • Tom Wolfe • Mario Puzo • Avery Corman • Judith Krantz • Larry McMurtry • Mary Higgins Clark • Stephen King • Peter Benchley • Ray Bradbury • Sidney Sheldon • Maya Angelou • Jane Goodall • Mark Mathabane • Loretta Lynn • Katherine Jackson • Carol Burnett • Kareem Abdul-Jabbar • Ted Williams • Ahmad Rashad • Abigail Van Buren • Priscilla Presley • Paul Monette • Robert Fulghum • Bill Cosby • Lucille Clifton • Robert Bly • Robert Frost • Nikki Giovanni • Langston Hughes • Joy Harjo • Edna St. Vincent Millay • William Carlos Williams • Terrence McNally • Jules Feiffer • Alfred Uhry • Horton Foote • Marsha Norman • Lynne Alvarez • Lonne Elder III • ntozake shange • Neil Simon • August Wilson • Harvey Fierstein • Beth Henley • David Mamet • Arthur Miller and Spike Lee.

New Writers' Voices—A series of anthologies and individual narratives by talented new writers. Stories, poems and true life experiences written by adult learners cover such topics as health, home and family, love, work, facing challenges and life in foreign countries. Many *New Writers' Voices* contain photographs and illustrations.

Reference—A reference library for adult new readers and writers. The first two books in the series are *How to Write a Play* and *Discovering Words: The Stories Behind English*.

Write for our free complete catalog:
LVNYC Publishing Program
121 Avenue of the Americas
New York, New York 10013